THE AVENGERS

WRITER
BRIAN MICHAEL BENDIS

PENCILER
WALTER SIMONSON

INKER
SCOTT HANNA

COLORIST
JASON KEITH

COVER ART
DANIEL ACUÑA (#25),
WALTER SIMONSON & PAUL MOUNTS (#26-28),
MIKE DEODATO & RAIN BEREDO (#29)
AND **LEINIL FRANCIS YU & SUNNY GHO** (#30)

LETTERER
VC'S CORY PETIT

ASSOCIATE EDITOR
LAUREN SANKOVITCH

EDITOR
TOM BREVOORT

Collection Editor: JENNIFER GRÜNWALD • Assistant Editors: ALEX STARBUCK & NELSON RIBEIRO
Editor, Special Projects: MARK D. BEAZLEY • Senior Editor, Special Projects: JEFF YOUNGQUIST
Senior Vice President of Sales: DAVID GABRIEL • SVP of Brand Planning & Communications: MICHAEL PASCIULLO

Editor in Chief: AXEL ALONSO • Chief Creative Officer: JOE QUESADA • Publisher: DAN BUCKLEY • Executive Producer: ALAN FINE

THE AVENGERS

28

EARTH'S MIGHTIEST HEROES, UNITED AGAINST A COMMON THREAT! ON THAT DAY THE AVENGERS WERE BORN, TO FIGHT FOES THAT NO SINGLE HERO COULD WITHSTAND!

IRON MAN

HAWKEYE

SPIDER-WOMAN

THE PROTECTOR

CAPTAIN AMERICA

STORM

THE RED HULK

PREVIOUSLY IN AVENGERS:
THE AVENGERS HAVE BEEN HARD AT WORK SAVING THE WORLD. BUT THE PUBLIC IS NOT HAPPY. ALL THEY SEE IS ONE CHAOTIC NEAR DISASTER AFTER ANOTHER.

CAPTAIN AMERICA IS THE HEAD OF THE AVENGERS AND MANY IN THE MEDIA BLAME HIM FOR THE STATE OF THINGS.

PREVIOUSLY IN AVENGERS VS X-MEN:
THE PHOENIX FORCE IS HEADED TOWARDS EARTH. THE AVENGERS BELIEVE THAT IT IS A DESTRUCTIVE FORCE THAT WILL LAY WASTE TO THE EARTH WHILE THE X-MEN BELIEVE IT TO BE A FORCE OF REBIRTH THAT COULD REIGNITE THE MUTANT RACE.

THE AVENGERS AND THE X-MEN BOTH BELIEVE IT WILL USE YOUNG MUTANT HOPE SUMMERS AS ITS AVATAR.

UTOPIA.
ISLAND HOME OF THE X-MEN.
OFF THE COAST OF SAN FRANCISCO.
NOW.

AVENGERS TOWER.
THEN.

CLANG

HEY! TRAINING ROBOTS DON'T GROW ON TREES, YOU KNOW, MISTER.

SORRY ABOUT THAT, TONY.

NO, NO, JUST TEASING... KNOCK YOURSELF OUT.

THAT'S WHAT THE FANCY NEW TRAINING ROOM IS FOR.

WHAT'S EATING YOU, CAP?

JUST BLOWING OFF SOME STEAM.

LIAR.

WHAT'S WRONG WITH HIM?

HE'S CRACKING UNDER THE PRESSURE.

OH, PLEASE, JESSICA.

WHAT?

CAPTAIN AMERICA DOES NOT CRACK UNDER PRESSURE.

OH, WAIT, I WAS THINKING OF ME.

HE'LL BE FINE, GUYS.

HEY, LISTEN, THIS JOB HE HAS RUNNING THE WORLD'S PEACEKEEPING TASKFORCES, IT WASN'T TOO LONG AGO THAT IT WAS MY JOB...

AND TRUST ME, IT'S NOT FUN BEING THE GUY THAT EVERYBODY BLAMES FOR EVERYTHING.

OH, IS THIS A THING WITH YOU TWO? HAWKEYE AND SPIDER-WOMAN ARE AN ITEM?

HMM?

OKAY THEN...

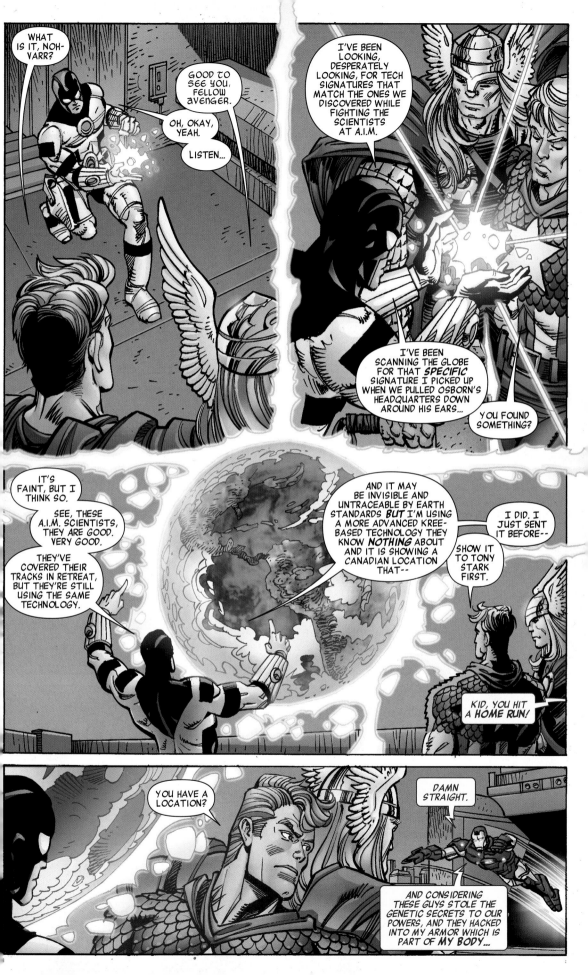

AGH!

OH GOD!

OH YEAH, DON'T NEED 'EM.

SURRENDER, TERRORISTS. BEFORE THIS GETS EVEN WORSE FOR YOU.

AGH!

FASHOO

I HAVE YOU, BRAVE AND FAIR MAIDEN.

WE ACCEPT YOUR SURRENDER.

NONE WAS OFFERED.

EITHER WAY.

WE ACCEPT YOUR SURRENDER.

BUT IF *ANY* OF YOU FEEL LIKE TRYING ANYTHING--

YES, GO FOR IT.

YOU KNOW YOUR SECRETS ARE NO LONGER YOURS.

WE HAVE THEM.

YOU OWN TODAY...BUT IT'S ONLY A MATTER OF TIME BEFORE THE PLAYING FIELD IS LEVELED AND YOU NO LONGER COUNT.

OKAY.

YOU LET US KNOW WHEN THAT HAPPENS.

WELL DONE, AVENGERS.

FEEL GOOD THIS DAY.

THOR'S RIGHT.

THAT IS JUST THE KIND OF CRAZY ONLY *WE* ARE IN A POSITION TO SHUT DOWN.

ESPECIALLY AS QUICKLY AND EXPERTLY AS YOU DID.

AND I MUST SAY: M.V.P. FOR THE DAY GOES TO NOH-VARR.

ABSOLUTELY.

WELL DONE, KID. YOU'VE GOT THE GOODS.

BUT SERIOUSLY, YOU HAVE *GOT* TO COME TO WORK FOR STARK RESILIENT.

I TOLD YOU.

I'M USING TECHNOLOGY THIS PLANET ISN'T *READY* FOR YET.

YOU HAVE TO EARN IT.

I WILL. I'LL *BUY* IT.

THANK YOU ALL.

IT'S HARD FOR ME TO EXPRESS MYSELF BUT I DO LOVE BEING PART OF ALL THIS.

I'VE LEARNED A LOT.

I'M SURE I HAVE *SOMETHING* HE WANTS.

NOT GOING TO HAPPEN.

LEAVE THE KID ALONE.

NOH-VARR, THE SUPREME INTELLIGENCE OF THE KREE EMPIRE WILL NOW ACKNOWLEDGE YOU.

YOU WERE PLACED ON EARTH BECAUSE THE EARTH IS, AND SHALL EVER BE, PROTECTED BY THE EMPIRE...BUT NOW A THREAT THAT SUPERSEDES YOUR MISSION IS UPON YOU.

THE PHOENIX FORCE, THE MOST DESTRUCTIVE COSMIC FORCE IN THE UNIVERSE, IS HEADED TOWARDS EARTH.

THE INTELLIGENCE HAS DECIDED THAT YOU, NOH-VARR, ARE TO INTERCEPT AND CONTAIN THE FORCE.

YOU WILL HELP THE EARTHLINGS IF IT HELPS YOU AND YOUR MISSION.

BUT IF ANYONE OR ANYTHING STANDS IN YOUR WAY, YOU ARE TO *ELIMINATE* THEM.

NOTHING IS MORE IMPORTANT TO THE EMPIRE, OR TO YOU, THAN THE INTERCEPTION AND CONTAINMENT OF THIS FORCE.

26

AVENGERS TOWER.

THE PHOENIX FORCE IS HEADED TOWARDS EARTH.

FOR THOSE UNFAMILIAR...IT'S A DESTRUCTIVE PARASITICAL FORCE OF COSMIC PROPORTIONS THAT LATCHES ON TO A BIOLOGICAL HOST--

--IT THEN USES THAT VESSEL TO LAY WASTE TO THE SURROUNDING ENVIRONMENT.

WE NEED TO DEAL WITH THIS IMMEDIATELY.

TONY STARK IS PUTTING A PLAN TOGETHER HERE ON EARTH BUT WE NEED TO SEND A TEAM INTO SPACE TO MEET IT HEAD-ON.

TO INTERCEPT IT.

TO ATTEMPT TO CONTAIN IT.

TO TRY AND DESTROY IT.

ONCE AND FOR ALL.

YOU, ALL OF YOU, BECAUSE OF YOUR OBVIOUS ABILITIES AND EXPERIENCE HAVE BEEN SELECTED FOR THAT MISSION.

I'M SORRY.

I WON'T LIE TO YOU...YOU'RE GOING HEAD-TO-HEAD WITH AN INDESTRUCTIBLE COSMIC FORCE...

IT IS BY DEFINITION A SUICIDE MISSION.

BUT IF YOU DON'T TRY...

IF SOMEONE DOESN'T TRY...

THERE WILL BE NO EARTH TO COME HOME TO.

LISTEN, GUYS, I CAN'T MAKE YOU GO...

OUR DUTY WILL BE MET.

OKAY THEN, YOU *LEAVE* IN ONE HOUR.

TAKE THAT TIME TO SETTLE YOUR AFFAIRS AS BEST YOU CAN.

I AM DONE WITH HIM.

WHO?

RICK. I'M DONE.

ALL OF A SUDDEN.

IT'S NOT "ALL OF A SUDDEN."

THE GUY DOESN'T EVEN PAY ATTENTION TO ME WHEN I'M TALKING.

SINCE WHEN? HE DOTES ON YOU.

DOTES. HE DOES NOT DOTE.

ALL HE DOES IS DOTE.

HEY, YOU...

ANNIE, MAY I SPEAK WITH YOU?

I'LL SEE YOU IN CLASS.

YEAH, UH, SURE...

"OOOH, LOOK AT ME, I'M DATING AN AVENGER."

"WHAT DO YOU MEAN YOU DON'T KNOW WHICH ONE HE IS?"

OKAY, SO, WHAT'S UP, NOH?

I HAVE TO LEAVE.

TOWN?

EARTH.

YOU'RE LEAVING THE PLANET?

WELL, IT'S NOT MY *HOME* PLANET.

YEAH, I KNOW.

BUT--BUT YOU SAID YOU WERE STAYING. YOU SAID--

IT'S A MISSION.

FOR THE AVENGERS.

YES.

OH, OKAY, THAT'S DIFFERENT. SORRY, I THOUGHT--

WELL, I HAVE FINALS AND THREE PAPERS DUE THIS MONTH SO I WASN'T GOING TO BE THE BEST GIRLFRIEND ANYWAY SO--

I DON'T KNOW WHEN I'M COMING BACK.

WAIT, ARE YOU *EVER* COMING BACK?

ARE YOU EVER COMING BACK?

I DON'T THINK SO.

OH.

I DIDN'T WANT TO LEAVE WITHOUT TELLING YOU.

WELL, UH, OKAY.

THANKS. I GUESS.

IF THERE'S ANY WAY TO GET BACK, I WILL.

IS THERE-- IS THERE ANY--? I MEAN, IS IT LIKE A SUICIDE MISSION TYPE OF DEAL?

CAPTAIN AMERICA THINKS SO.

OH, WELL... HE WOULD KNOW.

I'M SORRY.

I DON'T KNOW WHAT TO DO.

WHAT IS IT?

IT'S YOURS UNTIL I GET BACK.

BUT WHAT IS IT?

I'LL TELL YOU WHEN NEXT I SEE YOU.

ANNIE.

THANK YOU.

YOU HAVE NO IDEA HOW DIFFICULT IT WAS FOR ME TO ACCLIMATE TO THIS WORLD. YOU HAVE NO IDEA WHAT A GIFT YOU HAVE BEEN TO ME.

GOOD-BYE.

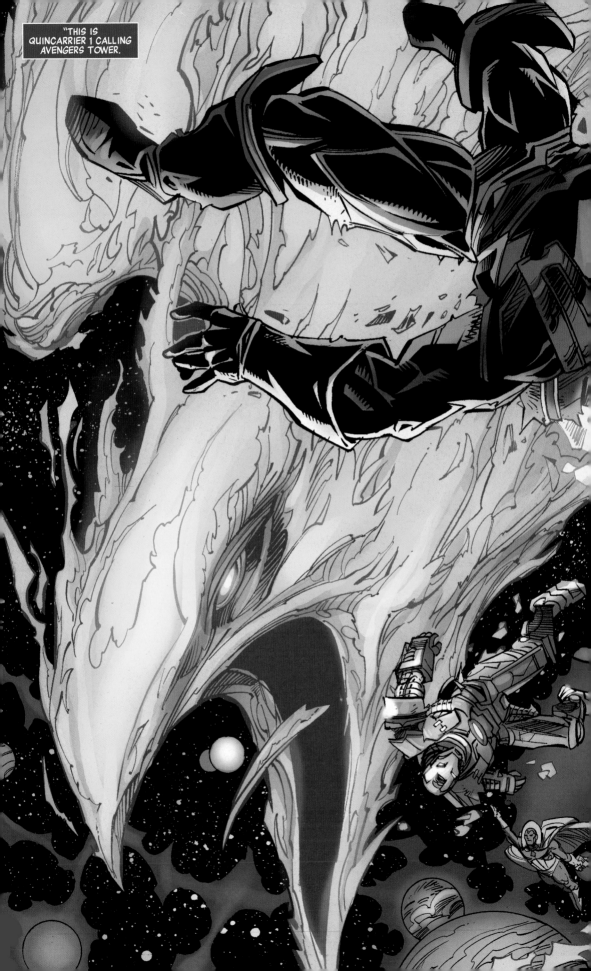

"IF YOU CAN HEAR ME, TONY, CAP, JARVIS, IF YOU ARE RECEIVING THIS TRANSMISSION, BE AWARE.

"WE FAILED.

"WE COMPLETELY FAILED AT OUR MISSION."

FOR DETAILS, SEE **SECRET AVENGERS #26-28** ON SALE NOW!

DAMN IT!

HANK, COME ON!

WE KNEW IT WAS A LONG SHOT.

IT WAS AND IS A SUICIDE MISSION. WE'RE LUCKY TO BE ALIVE.

WE SHOULD HEAD BACK TO EARTH AND HELP WHERE WE CAN.

YOU UNDERSTAND THAT OUR FAILURE TO SEE OUR MISSION THROUGH MEANS *THERE WON'T BE AN EARTH TO GO BACK TO!*

"AND WE'LL BE STUCK ON THIS MADHOUSE OF A PLANET!"

I'LL GO TALK TO HIM.

HE DIDN'T MEAN ANYTHING ABOUT THE KREE HOMEWORLD, YOU KNOW, HE'S JUST UPSET.

AND WITH EVERYTHING WE'VE BEEN THROUGH HERE...

I SHOULD REPORT TO THE SUPREME INTELLIGENCE.

WHY?

...

WHY WOULDN'T WE?

CAN WE EVEN CONTACT CAPTAIN AMERICA OR TONY STARK FROM THIS FAR OUT?

I RAN THE NUMBERS AGAIN AND AGAIN...

DO YOU THINK THEY HEARD US?

IT'S UNLIKELY FROM THIS DISTANCE, VALKYRIE. NOT WITH THIS EQUIPMENT.

WILL THE KREE HELP US? I KNOW THEY HAVE THEIR HANDS FULL BUT--

HOLD ON...

WHAT IS IT?

I'M TRYING TO CALCULATE WHERE WE WENT WRONG.

THIS CONTAINMENT UNIT BEAST BUILT *SHOULD* HAVE BEEN ABLE TO CONTAIN SOME OF THE PHOENIX.

IT'S BUILT TO FOLD THAT EXACT ENERGY SIGNATURE ONTO ITSELF AND NEGATE IT.

IT DOESN'T MAKE SENSE THAT--HUH.

WHAT SAY YOU?

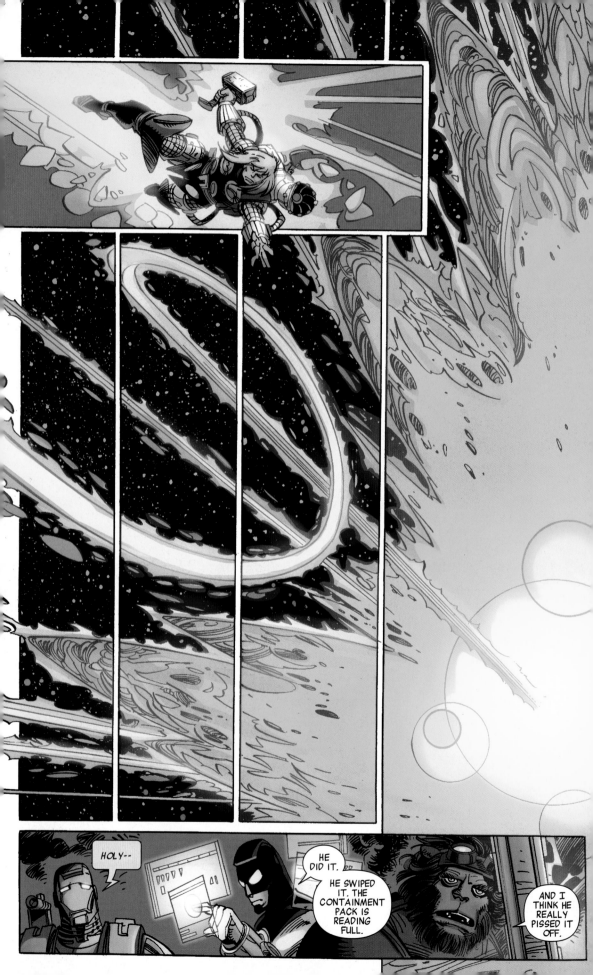

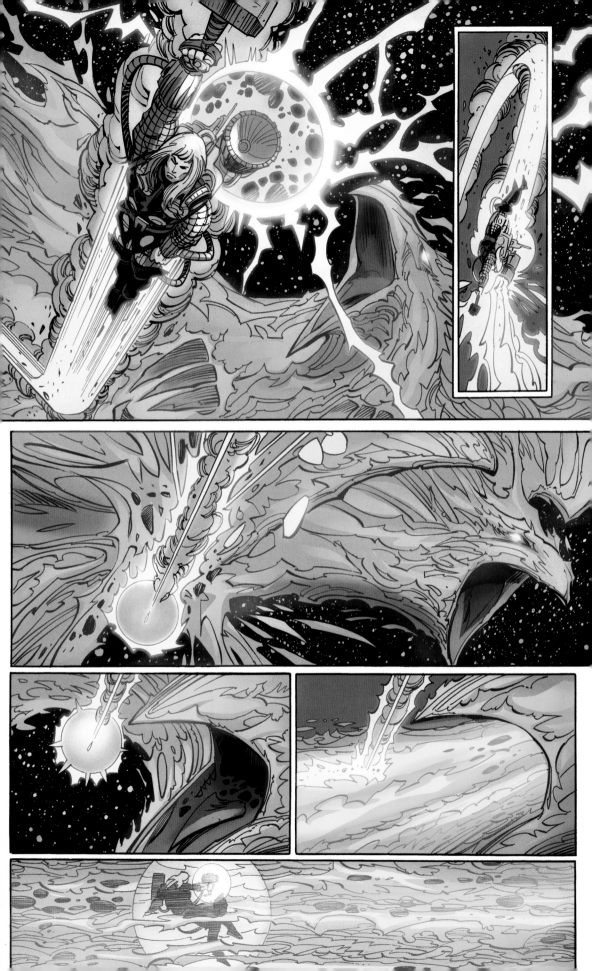

WELL DONE, GOOD FELLOW.

CAREFUL, CAREFUL...

I'VE NEVER SEEN HIM SO BEATEN...

IT RAN AWAY, RIGHT?

THE PHOENIX JUST UP AND RAN AWAY FROM HIM.

THOR, BUDDY, CAN YOU HEAR ME?

THOR?

I--I CLIPPED ITS WING.

IT... IT CAN BE BESTED.

I SAY WE GET OUR ASSES IN GEAR AND FLY THIS THING RIGHT BACK TO EARTH...

WE SHOW THIS TO TONY STARK AND HANK PYM...

AND I GUARANTEE YOU BY 6 O'CLOCK TONIGHT THEY'LL KNOW EXACTLY HOW TO SHUT THIS DAMN THING DOWN FOR GOOD.

EXCEPT I CAN'T LET YOU DO THAT.

GOD OF THUNDER, YOU SLEEP SO PEACEFULLY.

LADY SIF... YOU LOOK TRANSCENDENT.

DO YOU THINK IT WISE TO SLEEP NOW?

THE FIRE IS ABOUT TO CONSUME YOU.

IF YOU DON'T STOP IT, NO ONE WILL.

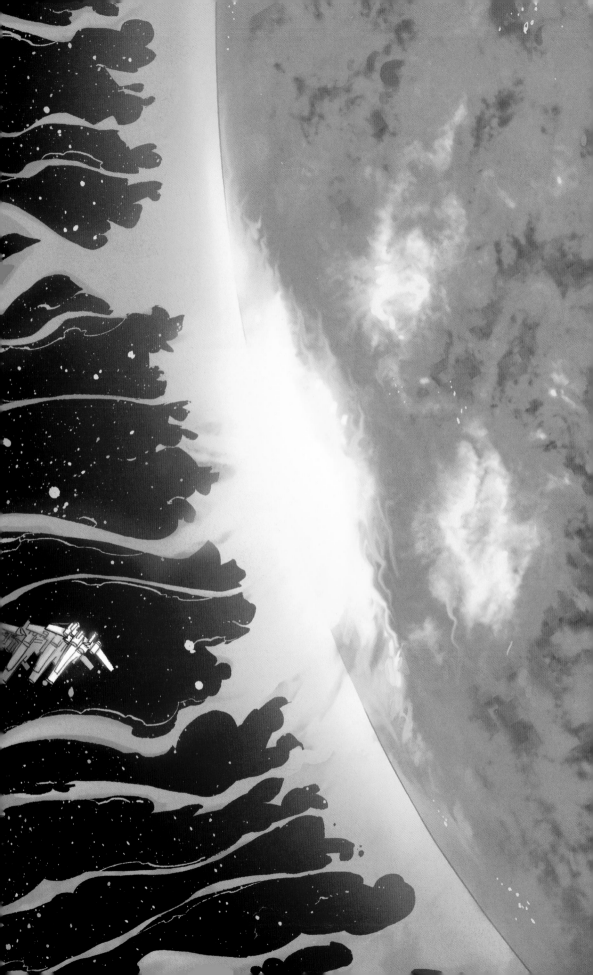

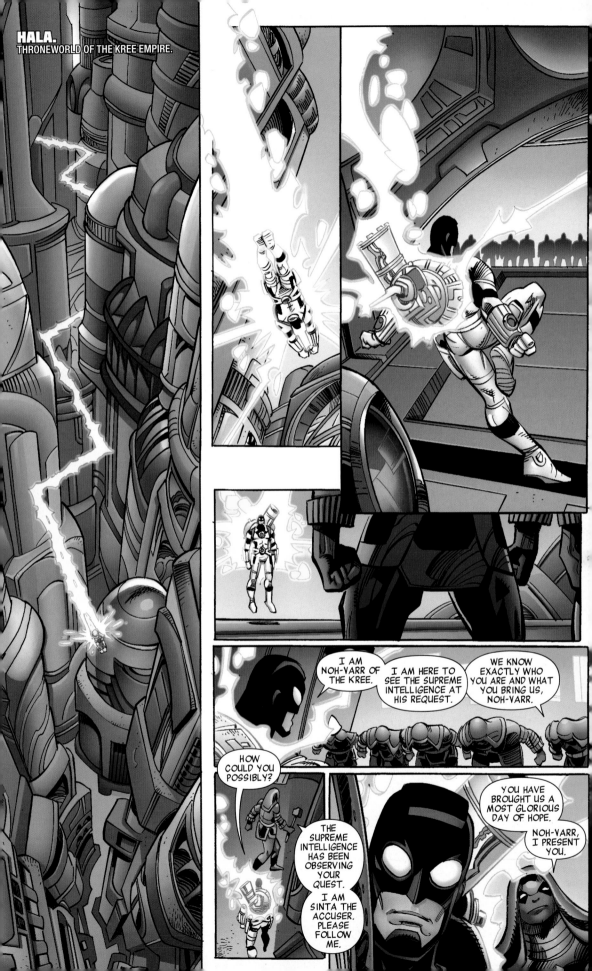

I AM NOH-VARR OF THE KREE.

I AM HERE TO SEE THE SUPREME INTELLIGENCE AT HIS REQUEST.

WE KNOW EXACTLY WHO YOU ARE AND WHAT YOU BRING US, NOH-VARR.

HOW COULD YOU POSSIBLY?

THE SUPREME INTELLIGENCE HAS BEEN OBSERVING YOUR QUEST.

I AM SINTA THE ACCUSER. PLEASE FOLLOW ME.

YOU HAVE BROUGHT US A MOST GLORIOUS DAY OF HOPE.

NOH-VARR, I PRESENT YOU.

NOH-VARR, THE SUPREME INTELLIGENCE OF THE KREE EMPIRE WILL NOW ACKNOWLEDGE YOU.

WE ARE PLEASED, SO PLEASED, BY YOUR COURSE OF ACTION THIS DAY.

YOU HAVE WITH YOU THE SAVIOR AND FUTURE OF THE ENTIRE EMPIRE.

THANK YOU, MOST KNOWLEDGABLE ONE. I AM HUMBLED BY YOUR GOOD WORDS.

THIS PORTION OF THE PHOENIX FORCE THE EARTHERS WERE ABLE TO REMOVE IS A SEED FROM WHICH GREAT POWER WILL GROW.

THE HIGH COUNCIL IS GATHERING THE GREATEST SCIENTIFIC MINDS OF ALL THE WORLD AND ALL THE CULTURES UNDER THE EMPIRE'S RULE.

WITH THAT AND MY ALREADY PROFOUND INTELLECTUAL ABILITIES, WE WILL USE THIS SAMPLE TO CREATE A CONTAINMENT OF THE ENTIRE PHOENIX FORCE.

THEN WE WILL USE THE FORCE FOR THE EMPIRE'S INTERESTS FOR MILLENNIA TO COME.

I-- I DON'T UNDERSTAND.

THE KREE EMPIRE WILL BE THE OWNER AND CONTROLLER OF THE PHOENIX.

THE DAYS OF WAR AND CONQUEST WILL BE A THING OF THE PAST.

BUT--BUT WE NEED TO USE THIS TO FIND A WAY TO SAVE THE EARTH.

THAT IS NOT POSSIBLE NOW.

THE EARTH IS UNDER THE PROTECTION OF THE KREE..

YOU SENT ME TO EARTH TO PROTECT IT.

YOU WERE PROTECTING THEM FROM THEMSELVES AND FROM THOSE WHO WOULD USE THEIR RESOURCES AGAINST US.

AND YOU WERE SUCCESSFUL.

BY DOING SO IT REMOVES THE EARTH FROM OUR AND YOUR RESPONSIBILITIES.

BUT THE PHOENIX HAS CHOSEN THE EARTH FOR CONSUMPTION.

YOU NOH-VARR, HAVE BOUGHT US THAT TIME.

WE BELIEVE THAT THE PHOENIX'S HUNGER, LIKE THAT OF THE WORLD EATER GALACTUS, WILL BE TEMPORARILY SATIATED, GIVING US THE TIME WE NEED TO PLAN AND EXECUTE THAT PLAN.

YOU--
YOU--

PLEASE, I MADE A TERRIBLE MISTAKE.

WE TRUSTED YOU. WE MADE YOU ONE OF US.

DO WHAT YOU MUST.

WE SHOULD TAKE YOU BACK TO EARTH AND MAKE YOU PAY FOR YOUR CRIMES.

YES. TAKE ME BACK TO EARTH. TAKE ME. I'LL FIX THIS.

I'LL MAKE IT RIGHT.

RRRRNO!!

YOU STAY AWAY FROM EARTH!

NEVER AGAIN! YOU UNDERSTAND?!

YOU STAY AWAY FROM US OR I'LL KILL YOU MYSELF!

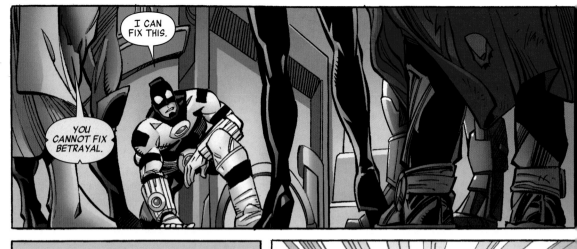

I CAN FIX THIS.

YOU CANNOT FIX BETRAYAL.

WHACK

YOU STAY AWAY FROM US AND YOU STAY AWAY FROM EARTH.

YOU LOST YOUR EARTH PRIVILEGES.

AND YOU'RE DAMN LUCKY THE HULK OR WOLVERINE WASN'T HERE.

YOU'D BE DEAD.

BETRAYER!

INFIDEL!

HE ATTACKED THE INTELLIGENCE!

THOSE NEGA-BANDS WERE THE PURVIEW OF THE INTELLIGENCE.

AND NOW YOU'VE *BETRAYED* YOUR PEOPLE.

ARE YOU SUCH A FOOL THAT YOU THINK YOU WOULD BE ABLE TO *KEEP THEM?*

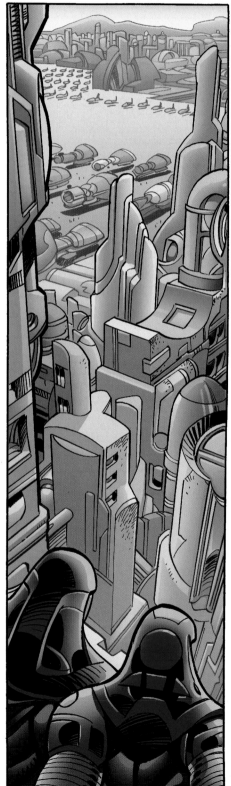

GOOD RIDDANCE.

DON'T BE A FOOL.

HE'S OUT THERE SOMEWHERE.

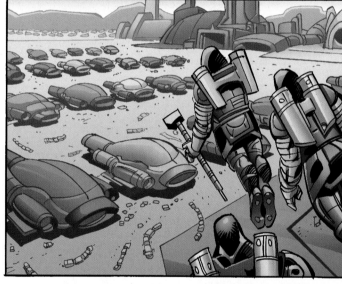

I WANT YOU ALL TO SPLIT UP INTO FOUR GROUPS AND I WANT YOU TO SCOUR THE CHAMBER GROUNDS.

I HEARD HE KILLED HIMSELF.

UNTIL A BODY IS FOUND I WANT YOU TO DO WHAT YOU ARE TOLD.

RED HULK

IRON MAN

HAWKEYE

CAPTAIN AMERICA

BLACK PANTHER

PREVIOUSLY:

THE PHOENIX FORCE HAS ARRIVED, IMBUING FIVE OF THE MOST ICONIC MUTANTS -- CYCLOPS, EMMA FROST, NAMOR, COLOSSUS AND MAGIK -- WITH WORLD-ALTERING POWERS.

THE AVENGERS WISH TO NEUTRALIZE THE COSMIC FORCE, BUT ARE PUT IN A PRECARIOUS SITUATION AS THE MUTANTS HAVE THUS FAR BEEN USING THEIR POWERS FOR HUMANITARIAN EFFORTS ACROSS THE GLOBE. AS EARTH'S MIGHTIEST HEROES SEEM OVERPOWERED AND OUTMANEUVERED IN EVERY HEAD-TO-HEAD CONFRONTATION, SOME SEE A SHIFT IN TACTICS AS THE ONLY POSSIBLE SOLUTION.

THE AVENGERS
VERSUS
THE X-MEN.

THIS ISN'T
WHAT I AM.

WHAT AM I
DOING HERE?

I KEEP TRYING TO GO OVER
THE EVENTS IN MY HEAD--
EVERYTHING SINCE THE
PHOENIX TOUCHED THE EARTH
AND THE PHOENIX AND THE
X-MEN BECAME ONE.

SINCE CAPTAIN AMERICA
DECLARED WAR ON THEM
BECAUSE THEY LEFT HIM
NO CHOICE.

BUT I CAN'T WRAP MY
HEAD AROUND IT BECAUSE ALL
I DO IS FIGHT. THE AVENGERS
KEEP THROWING ME INTO
BATTLE--ONE AFTER THE NEXT.

WHY? BECAUSE I AM A *HULK*.
THAT IS HOW THEY SEE ME.

A BLUNT
INSTRUMENT.
A PIT BULL.

I GET THAT. I *AM* A HULK.
WHICH IS STILL ONE OF
GOD'S TOP TEN CRUELEST
JOKES OF ALL TIME.

I SPENT THE ENTIRETY
OF MY LIFE CHASING THE
ORIGINAL GREEN HULK,
BRUCE BANNER, ACROSS EVERY
DESERT IN THIS COUNTRY.

LOOKING FOR A WAY
TO END THE HULK AND
NOW I *AM* A HULK.

BUT CAPTAIN AMERICA
KNOWS WHO I REALLY
AM. HE KNOWS BEFORE
THIS I WAS THUNDERBOLT
ROSS, A DECORATED
GENERAL IN THE MOST
MAGNIFICENT ARMY IN
THE WORLD.

I WAS--I *AM* A WAR
HERO. NOTHING CAN TAKE
THAT AWAY FROM ME.

I HAVE MORE MEDALS
THAN I COULD EVER
WEAR ON MY UNIFORM.

AND CAPTAIN
AMERICA WANTS
ME HERE.

BUT WHY ME?
WHY NOW? WHY
AM I HERE?

CIRCUMSTANCE? NO.

THE REAL QUESTION IS: WHAT DO I HAVE TO BRING TO THE TABLE OTHER THAN THE HULK?

MILITARY EXPERIENCE.

I HAVE AS MUCH MILITARY EXPERIENCE AS CAPTAIN AMERICA.

I MIGHT HAVE MORE.

HE *IS* A CAPTAIN. I'M A GENERAL.

SO I PROBABLY HAVE AS MUCH MILITARY EXPERIENCE AS ANYONE WHO'S EVER BEEN AN AVENGER.

UNLESS YOU COUNT WAR CRIMES... AND I DON'T.

OR WAR PROFITEERING... AND I DON'T.

BUT WHETHER OR NOT THESE PEOPLE WOULD FOLLOW *ME* INTO BATTLE AT THIS POINT IN MY AVENGERS CAREER I DO NOT KNOW. PROBABLY NOT.

NOT WITHOUT CAPTAIN AMERICA STANDING THERE DEMANDING THEY RESPECT ME.

BUT I SEE IT IN THEIR EYES. THEY HAVE NO IDEA WHO I AM OR WHY I'M HERE OR WHY CAPTAIN AMERICA PUTS VALUE IN MY OPINION OVER THEIRS.

THEY DO NOT GET IT. THIS IS WAR.

I ADVISE CAPTAIN AMERICA IN ANY WAY HE NEEDS. BUT I LOOK AT THE CAPTAIN AND I FEEL *THAT'S* NOT REALLY THE REASON I'M HERE EITHER, FOR ALL OF CAPTAIN AMERICA'S IMPRESSIVE QUALITIES AS A SOLDIER, THERE ARE THINGS I WOULD DO THAT HE NEVER WOULD.

HE LOOKS AT ME AND I SEE THAT LOOK IN HIS EYES.

HE *NEEDS* SOMETHING FROM ME. HE NEEDS ME TO TAKE IT SOMEWHERE HE CAN'T GO...

THAT'S IT, THEN, ISN'T IT?

THEN I KNOW *EXACTLY* WHAT I HAVE TO DO.

I HAVE TO GO WHERE CAPTAIN AMERICA CAN'T AND WHERE WOLVERINE WON'T...

I JUST NEED TO WAIT FOR MY MOMENT TO STRIKE.

THERE ARE FIVE MUTANT LEADERS: CYCLOPS, EMMA FROST, MAGIK, NAMOR AND COLOSSUS. EACH HAS A PIECE OF THE PHOENIX FORCE UNDER THEIR CONTROL.

FIGHTING COLOSSUS *BEFORE* THE PHOENIX FORCE ALMOST BROKE ME. I DO NOT WANT TO TAKE THE CHANCE WITH HIM NOW.

NAMOR TOO. AND MAGIK? I HATE MAGIC. I HATE MAGIC ANYTHING. I CAN'T FIGHT RANDOM CHAOS.

SO I HAVE TO WAIT UNTIL THEY ARE ALL SEPARATED. WHICH WON'T BE HARD BECAUSE THEY HAVE THEIR OWN AGENDAS.

INTEL SHOWS THEY ARE EACH TRYING TO CARVE OUT A PIECE OF THE WORLD FOR THEMSELVES.

IF I HAVE ANY CHANCE AT THIS I NEED TO KNOW *FOR SURE* THAT EMMA FROST AND CYCLOPS ARE APART FROM EACH OTHER.

SHE CAN READ MINDS.

SHE'LL KNOW IF I'M ANYWHERE NEAR HIM.

I HAVE TO WAIT TILL THEY SEPARATE IF I'LL HAVE A CHANCE TO--

MAGNETO.

THE MUTANT MASTER OF MAGNETISM.

I WAS PREPARED.

NOTHING METAL ON ME.

NOT MY KNIFE MADE OF BONE OR MY GUN MADE OF FIBERGLASS.

THE FILES SAID IF HE WAS ON THE ISLAND, AND THAT EVEN IF HE NEVER SAW ME HE COULD SENSE THE METAL.

HE WOULD FEEL IT.

HE WOULD KILL ME WITH MY OWN WEAPONS BEFORE I KNEW WHAT HAPPENED.

THIS IS THE MOST DANGEROUS GAME.

THIS IS A MINE FIELD.

EVERYWHERE I GO: MUTANTS.

EACH WITH ITS OWN POWER. EACH WITH ITS OWN SPECIALTY.

EVERY SECOND I SPEND ON UTOPIA I RISK DETECTION.

There he is: Cyclops, leader of the X-Men, in my sights. I take this decision very seriously.

This is a man's life. I have to weigh the greater good. I know this moment will haunt me for the rest of my life, like all the others. I have to imagine the lives saved by this one sacrifice. I know this man was a hero. I know he has sacrificed his life for the entire planet, over and over. I know he has loved. I know he has lost. I know he is a complicated man in a complicated time. But it doesn't matter what he *DID*. It matters what he is doing *NOW*. He is putting the entire world in grave danger. He won't stop so I have to stop him. I have to put him down so the rest of us can see tomorrow.

IT WON'T MOVE.
MY FINGER WON'T--

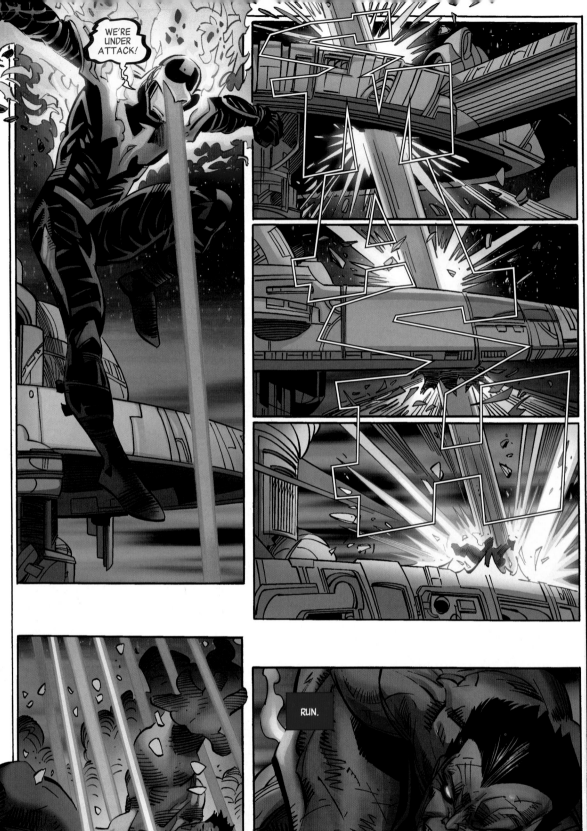

I ALWAYS THOUGHT CAPTAIN AMERICA HAD MORE CHARACTER THAN TO SEND AN ASSASSIN.

HE DOES.

YES. OUR JOLLY RED FRIEND IS HERE OF HIS OWN VOLITION.

THEN WE HAVE A PRISONER OF WAR.

WE CAN'T HOLD HIM.

SHE'S RIGHT!

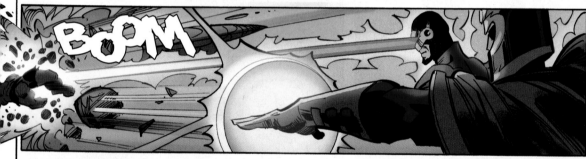

BOOM

GET RID OF HIM. GET HIM OUT OF HERE.

HE STEPPED INTO OUR YARD. THIS IS FAIR GAME. HE'S OUR PRISONER.

ACCORDING TO HIS OWN MEMORIES: HE'S BEATEN UP THE WATCHER AND SMACKED THE SILVER SURFER WITH HIS OWN BOARD. WE DON'T WANT HIM HERE.

SLIIICE

THEN WHAT DO WE DO WITH HIM?

HAARRGGHHH!!!

WAKANDA.

WHERE'S HOPE RIGHT NOW?

SHE'S SAFE, TONY.

I HATE HAVING HER OUT OF MY SIGHT.

WHEN I WAS IN BOOT CAMP, OUR LIEUTENANT SAID WORDS TO US THAT I DIDN'T UNDERSTAND WHEN I HEARD THEM BUT NOW ARE WORDS I LIVE BY...

SHE'S SAFE. LET'S GET BACK TO THE PLANS.

THE PLANS? WHAT PLANS?

LET'S DISCUSS OUR NEXT COURSE OF ACTION.

I THOUGHT WE WERE JUST WAITING AROUND FOR THE PHOENIX TO EAT US.

HE SAID: "FIGHTING IS THE MOST PRIMAL FORM OF HUMAN COMMUNICATION. IF YOU HAVE TO FIGHT, THAT MEANS THERE IS NO OTHER RECOURSE."

I KNOW YOU'RE TIRED, MY FRIEND. WE'RE ALL TIRED. BUT WE NEED TO--

BOOM

HOLY HELL!

TELL YOUR PEOPLE TO STAY BACK, T'CHALLA.

THEY BROUGHT THE WAR TO MY HOME.

SO IF YOU'RE READY TO FIGHT, YOU'D BETTER BE READY TO KILL.

29

WAKANDA.

ONE OF THE BIG REASONS THE X-MEN BEAT US AT EVERY TURN IS THAT THEY KNOW WHERE WE'RE GOING TO TURN BEFORE **WE** DO.

YEAH?

SORRY TO INTERRUPT, BUT I JUST HAD TO SAY WHAT'S ON MY--

YOU'RE NOT INTERRUPTING, SPIDER-WOMAN.

IF WE **HAD** SOMETHING RESEMBLING A PLAN YOU'D BE INTERRUPTING. BUT WE HAVE NOTHING.

WE'RE BRAINSTORMING.

I KNOW THIS SOUNDS PARANOID, BUT HEAR ME OUT.

WE CAN'T WIN THIS FIGHT THE WAY IT'S BEING FOUGHT.

AND NOT BECAUSE OF THE PHOENIX FORCE, EVEN THOUGH, SURE, YEAH, COSMIC DESTRUCTIVE FORCE...

BUT WE CAN'T WIN THE GROUND FIGHT AGAINST THE X-MEN BECAUSE THEY HAVE TELEPATHS AND WE DON'T.

NOW, SOME OF YOU KNOW, BEFORE I WAS AN AVENGER I WAS AN AGENT OF S.H.I.E.L.D....

AND BEFORE THAT I WAS AN AGENT OF HYDRA...

AND I HAVE BEEN THE VICTIM OF ENOUGH PSYCHIC MANIPULATION TO KNOW THAT ALL THEY NEED TO WIN IS PSYCHIC MANIPULATION.

SO, LET'S SAY THIS:

WHATEVER THIS PLAN YOU'RE COOKING UP IS, I RECOMMEND DOING A NICK FURY FIRST.

A NICK FURY?

MOAN ABOUT THE GOOD OLD DAYS?

I RECOMMEND GOING FOR THE TELEPATHS FIRST.

WHO *ARE* THE BIG TELEPATHS ON THE X-MEN?

HOLD ON, I'LL PULL UP THE INTEL...

EMMA FROST AND RACHEL SUMMERS.

YES, OKAY. *THOSE* SHOULD BE OUR PRIMARY TARGETS.

WE WON'T GET ANYWHERE *NEAR* SCOTT SUMMERS WITH *THOSE* TWO ON THE BOARD.

I DON'T DISAGREE

I THINK WE'RE A LITTLE PAST GETTING NEAR EMMA FROST.

TELL ME ABOUT IT!

I ASKED HER OUT FOUR TIMES OVER THE YEARS AND SHE SHOT ME DOWN *EVERY TIME.*

AND THAT WAS *BEFORE* SHE WAS A PHOENIX.

THAT'S BECAUSE SHE COULD READ YOUR MIND, SWEETIE.

IF I COULD READ YOUR MIND I WOULDN'T GO ANYWHERE NEAR YOU EITHER.

YOU HAVE *NO IDEA* HOW TRUE THAT IS.

I CAN DRAW OUT RACHEL.

WAIT.

DAMN.

I'VE ALREADY RUINED THE SCORE.

HOW SO?

BECAUSE NOW IF YOU GET *NEAR* SUMMERS SHE WILL READ YOUR MIND AND KNOW THAT *SHE* IS A TARGET.

SO NOW *WE* NEED A TELEPATH.

THERE'S 400 AVENGERS TEAMS... DO WE *HAVE* A TELEPATH?

A TELEPATH BETTER THAN *THEIR* TELEPATHS.

AND IF NOT, WHY NOT?

MOONDRAGON.

UH, ANYONE ELSE?

WHY, WHAT'S WRONG WITH *HER?*

ANYONE ELSE?

HER TOO?

YOU'RE SUCH A PIG.

LIKE YOU'RE A NUN.

ALL THE BEST ONES ARE MUTANTS.

WE WON'T BE ABLE TO TRUST THEM.

I CAN MAKE A CALL.

HE CAN MAKE A CALL.

SHE'S CLOSE.

I KNOW.

SHE WILL ALREADY BE ATTEMPTING TO READ YOUR THOUGHTS.

YUP.

I KNOW HOW THIS WORKS.

SHE WILL FEEL THAT SOMETHING IS DIFFERENT.

SHE WILL ASSUME THAT HENRY MCCOY IS ATTEMPTING TO USE PSYCHIC SHIELDS AGAINST HER.

LIKE I SAID, BUB, I KNOW HOW THIS WORKS.

LONG WAY TO GO FOR A TRAP.

IT ONLY WORKS IF SHE THINKS LOGAN'S ON THE LAM, WAR MACHINE.

I KNOW HOW IT WORKS.

IT'S STILL A LONG WAY TO GO.

SHH.

I KNOW HOW MUCH YOU RESPECT HER.

LET'S JUST GET THIS OVER WITH.

SHE'S HERE.

IT'S NOT *YOUR* TRAP... IT'S *HERS.*

YEAH, I JUST CAUGHT THAT.

YOU'VE LOST YOUR WAY IN THIS FIGHT, LOGAN.

YOU'RE LETTING YOUR PERSONAL RESENTMENT OF CYCLOPS CLOUD YOUR *JUDGMENT.*

THE PHOENIX IS HERE TO *SAVE* US. TO MAKE CERTAIN THE FUTURE I CAME FROM NEVER COMES TO BE.

WHY WOULD YOU WANT TO STAND IN THE WAY OF TRUE UTOPIA?

THIS WAS A *MISTAKE.*

TOO LATE.

THE PHOENIX AIN'T ON OUR SIDE, DARLIN'.

IT'S ON ITS *OWN.*

AND YOU'RE THE ONE WHO'S LOST THEIR DAMNED WAY.

I'M JUST GLAD YOUR *MOMMA* AIN'T HERE TO SEE THIS.

HENRY... YOU'RE ONE OF MY OLDEST FRIENDS IN THE WORLD. I'M NOT GOING TO FIGHT YOU.

WELL, THIS GOT UGLY FAST.

AS I FEARED IT WOULD.

WE SHOULD GET THESE PEOPLE OUT OF--

KA-BOOM

DEAR LORD, I'M SO SORRY.

IT IS NOT YOUR FAULT. YOU SAVED US.

CAN WE GET ON WITH THIS?

WAIT! THOR'S GOT HER ON THE ROPES.

IF GOD BOY SCORES A TAKEDOWN WE MAY NOT HAVE TO GO THROUGH WITH THE WHOLE...

THOR WOULD RATHER FIGHT WOMEN THAN FACE THE KING OF ATLANTIS!

WHY AM I NOT SURPRISED? IMPERIUS REX!

SCRATCH THAT.

IT'S NOW OR NEVER, BIG BRAIN.

KEEP THE OTHERS OCCUPIED.

I HAVE HER.

NO!!

JESSICA DREW, HOW ARE YOU STILL AWAKE?

PSYCHIC SHIELDS. PRETTY GOOD ONES.

HAD THEM IMPLANTED WHEN I WAS AN AGENT OF S.H.I.E.L.D.

WE'RE SO CLOSE TO SHUTTING THIS DOWN.

WHAT *CAN'T* YOU DO?

I CAN'T RAISE MY HAND TO MY STUDENTS.

I CAN'T FIGHT THIS FIGHT.

I CAN'T BE PART OF THIS.

I WAS WRONG TO COME HERE.

THAT'S NOT TRUE. WE *NEED* YOU.

THEY--*THEY* NEED YOU.

THEY NEED HELP GETTING OUT FROM UNDER THIS PHOENIX INFLUENCE...

THEY ARE GROWN MEN AND WOMEN.

THEY HAVE MADE THEIR CHOICES.

WAIT, NO, I'M NOT SAYING THIS--THIS IS NOT YOUR FAULT, PROFESSOR.

YOU'RE RIGHT. THEY *ARE* GROWN MEN AND WOMEN.

BUT WE NEED YOU TO *SHUT THEM DOWN.*

WE-- THEY--WE NEED HELP.

I DON'T HAVE THE TASTE FOR MADNESS AND BLOOD THE REST OF YOU DO.

CAPTAIN AMERICA, WAKE UP. I WANT YOU TO HEAR THIS.

30

A SERIOUS PLAY.

A GAME-CHANGING PLAY.

NEW YORK HARBOR.

AND I DO LOVE AN OPPORTUNITY.

NORTH CONCOURSE SECURE.

AGAIN. AS ALWAYS.

OKAY, DON'T ANSWER ME.

I GET PAID EITHER WAY.

GKKSS!

SHLCK

THE OUTER PERIMETER IS SECURE, MASTER.

THEN LET'S PROCEED, SHALL WE?

SLIIICEEE

HOW COME NO ONE IS ANSWERING THE--

WHAT THE--?

AAGGH!!

SLICEE

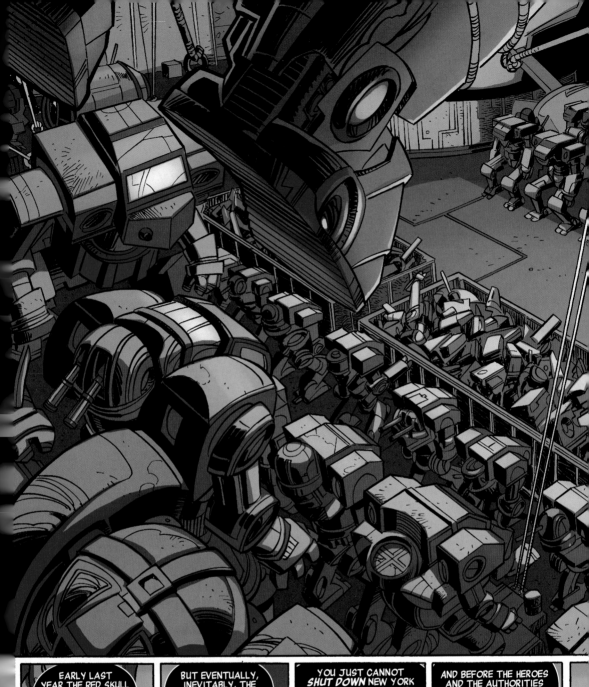

EARLY LAST YEAR THE RED SKULL MADE A VERY BOLD TERRORIST ATTACK ON THE EASTERN SEABOARD.

USING THESE VERY HIGH-TECH, MAN-DRIVEN, WEAPONIZED VEHICLES.

AND IN THE NAME OF THE LEGACY OF HER FÜHRER THE RED SKULL ALMOST ACHIEVED HER GOAL.

BUT EVENTUALLY, INEVITABLY, THE AVENGERS AND S.H.I.E.L.D. WERE ABLE TO END HER MADNESS.

NOW WHAT YOU MIGHT NOT KNOW IS, AFTER IT WAS ALL OVER, THE "HEROES" AND THE AUTHORITIES HAD TO CLEAN UP THE CITY FAST.

YOU JUST CANNOT SHUT DOWN NEW YORK CITY FOR EVEN AN HOUR-- THE GLOBAL MARKET BUTTERFLY EFFECT WOULD BE ASTRONOMICAL!

SO THEY HAD THESE BEAUTIFUL WEAPONS PULLED OFF THE STREETS AND SHOVED INTO HIDDEN WAREHOUSES JUST LIKE THIS ONE.

AND BEFORE THE HEROES AND THE AUTHORITIES COULD FIGURE OUT WHAT TO DO NEXT, THEY WERE ON TO THE NEXT CATASTROPHE.

SO HERE THEY SIT--WHAT'S LEFT OF THE RED SKULL'S MAGNIFICENT ARMY.

THIS TECHNOLOGY, THIS WEAPONRY, IS, I AM TOLD, AN ENTIRE GENERATION AHEAD OF ANYTHING THAT THE ARMED FORCES OF THE UNITED STATES IS USING.

WHACK

HA!

ARE YOU NOT *TALKING* TO ME NOW?

I WASN'T TALKING TO YOU *ALL DAY* BUT YOU DIDN'T *NOTICE* BECAUSE YOU NEVER STOPPED *TALKING* LONG ENOUGH TO FIGURE IT OUT!

WHAT ARE YOU SO MAD ABOUT?

CAN YOU GUYS *BELIEVE* THIS?!

KEEP *THEM* OUT OF THIS!

YOU KNOW, WHEN YOU TEAM UP WITH SPIDER-MAN YOU GET SOME WITTY BANTER GOING. SURE IT'S NOT ALL *GOLD* BUT IT'S STILL--

SHUT UP!

CRAZY LADY.

AND LET ME GIVE YOU SOME *ADVICE*, ROMEO!

YOU DON'T ASK WOMEN ABOUT THEIR *PERIODS*!

YOU *DON'T* COMPLIMENT THEIR SISTER!

YOU-- YOU DON'T *EVER*--

--EVER--

--CALL US CRAZY.

SERIOUSLY, CAN YOU GUYS BELIEVE THIS?

ON MANY LEVELS...I CANNOT.

DAMN IT, I LIKE YOU, ALL RIGHT!

NOT YOU, I DON'T KNOW YOU.

YEAH? SO WHAT'S GOING ON WITH YOU AND THE SCARLET WITCH?

UH-OH.

YEAH, UH-OH.

YOU DIDN'T THINK THAT TELLING ME YOU HAD AN UNRESOLVED SITUATION WITH HER WAS A GOOD IDEA?

UH...

IT'S NOT LIKE THAT.

YEAH?

WHAT'S IT LIKE?

WHAT DID SHE SAY?

YOU MEAN: WHAT DID SHE SAY ON OUR ALL-DAY RIDE HOME IN THE QUINJET?

WHERE ALL SHE TALKED ABOUT WAS YOU?

YOU GUYS AREN'T GOING TO TELL ANYONE ABOUT THIS, RIGHT?

BRO CODE?

WHERE SHE SAID: I WONDER WHAT THINGS ARE GOING TO BE LIKE BETWEEN YOU TWO NOW THAT SHE IS BACK WITH THE AVENGERS?

AND I SAID: WHATEVER DO YOU MEAN?

SHE SAYS: WELL WE HAVE SOME UNRESOLVED ISSUES IN THAT WE USED TO HAVE A THING.

BUT HER KNOWING YOU AS WELL AS SHE DOES, SHE'S WONDERING IF AND WHEN IT'LL EVER RESOLVE ITSELF...

THIS THING WITH YOU AND HER...

AND WHAT DID I THINK OF THE WHOLE THING?

YOU KNOW, ME BEING A WOMAN OF THE WORLD.

WHAT DID YOU SAY?

I SAID I WANTED TO LIGHT YOU ON FIRE.

SO YOU'RE UPSET WITH ME?

WOW, SHERLOCK, FIGURED THAT OUT, DID YA?

YOU'RE MAD AT ME FOR EXISTING BEFORE WE HOOKED UP?

YOU KNOW WHAT?

I'VE--

WAIT.

WAIT?

NEVER MIND.

I TAKE IT BACK.

I TAKE IT ALL BACK.

WHAT'S HAPPENING NOW?

THIS ISN'T ME.

THIS IS NOT WHAT I WANT TO ACT LIKE.

IN FACT, I PROMISED MYSELF I WOULD *NEVER* ACT LIKE THIS OR SOUND LIKE THIS.

I DON'T KNOW WHAT'S WRONG WITH ME.

FIRST OF ALL, WE'RE EXHAUSTED. YOU'RE *ALLOWED* TO BE EXHAUSTED.

LISTEN. HEY, I LIKE YOU.

I'M WITH YOU.

SO STOP TRYING TO RUIN US.

WHY DOES EVERYTHING HAVE TO BE SO--WHY CAN'T I JUST ONCE IN *MY LIFE* HAVE SOMETHING JUST BE--

I CAN'T APOLOGIZE FOR MY PAST.

AND YOU CAN'T EITHER.

HEY, YOU WERE AN AGENT OF S.H.I.E.L.D. *AND* AN AGENT OF HYDRA...

WHO THE HELL KNOWS WHAT *YOU'VE* BEEN UP TO OUT IN THE FIELD?

WE RUN IN A TIGHT CIRCLE.

AND THERE'S ONLY SO MANY PEOPLE WE CAN TRUST AND SO MANY PEOPLE WE'RE GOING TO BE ABLE TO CONNECT WITH.

AND AS FOR WANDA?

I KNOW... I *KNOW!*

HAVE YOU NOT BEEN PAYING ATTENTION THE LAST COUPLE OF YEARS?

SHE'S GOT SOME *ISSUES!*

HER FATHER SCREWED HER UP SO BAD.

THE ONLY PERSON WHOSE FATHER SCREWED THEM UP *MORE* THAN HER FATHER SCREWED HER UP, IS HOW MUCH *YOUR* FATHER SCREWED YOU UP.

WELL HE DID EXPERIMENT ON ME IN THE WOMB.

YEAH, AND LOOK AT YOU NOW: YOU'RE DOING AMAZING!

BUT YOU THINK MAYBE YOUR ISSUES WITH MEN MIGHT STEM FROM THAT ONE FACT?

DON'T HIT ME.

HO, FELLOW AVENGERS!

WHAT SAY THEE?

I'M ZONKED.

MASTER THOR, WOULD YOU CARE FOR SOME MEAD AND BRISKET?

I WOULD, GOOD JARVIS.

ANYONE SEEN BARTON?

HE AND SPIDER-WOMAN WENT ON A MISSION, MASTER STARK.

I BET THEY DID.

THIS IS ROGERS.

WHERE?

YEAH, NO. WE HAVE IT.

SUIT UP, GENTLEMEN.

THERE'S BEEN A BREAK-IN AT ONE OF S.H.I.E.L.D.'S SECRET WAREHOUSES IN THE CITY.

CAN'T S.H.I.E.L.D. TAKE CARE OF IT?

NOT THIS WAREHOUSE.

UGH...

AVENGERS ASSEMBLE.

YES?

JESSICA, DARLING, WELL DONE.

THE BAD GUY IS VANQUISHED ONCE AGAIN.

AVENGERS ASSEMBLE AND ALL THAT.

WHAT WAS THIS ABOUT?

JUST DOING MY PART.

SO THIS BENEFITED YOU HOW?

BENEFITED ME?

LADY, YOU DON'T DO ANYTHING UNLESS IT BENEFITS YOU AND "THE CAUSE."

WELL, I WILL ADMIT, YOU HAVE REMOVED A POTENTIAL COMPETITOR OFF THE TABLE WHILE HYDRA GETS OUR DUCKS IN A ROW.

THESE WANNABE KINGPINS--YOU DANGLE JUST A TINY LITTLE BIT OF INTEL UNDER THEIR NOSE AND THEY JUST *JUMP* RIGHT IN.

WHY DIDN'T YOU JUST TAKE HIM OUT YOURSELF?

BECAUSE, JESSICA, I'M ALWAYS LOOKING OUT FOR YOU.

NO MATTER WHAT YOU THINK OF YOURSELF WE ALWAYS CONSIDER YOU ONE OF US.

BULL!

NO, I MEAN IT.

**#25 AVENGERS ART APPRECIATION VARIANT
BY GABRIELE DELL'OTTO**